edited by
Anne-Marie Choong
Tandip Singh Mann

This book belongs to:

....

_____

Accelerated Education Publications Ltd.

Contents

510.71 CUR
EDUCATION. TW

Chapter Four
FRACTIONS
1. What is a Fraction?

A Fraction is part of a Whole. It has a top and bottom half.

$\dfrac{1}{2}$

1 - **Numerator** (How many parts)

2 - **Denominator** (Total number of parts)

Examples: | Express as Fractions a) A Whole One b) A Half.

a) **One Whole**

$\dfrac{1}{1}$ (One part) of (One part)

b) **One Half**

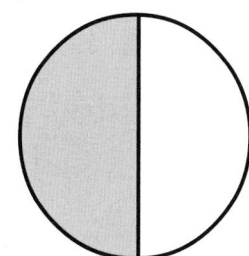

$\dfrac{1}{2}$ (One part) of (Two parts)

> Circles are used to represent Fractions. A Fraction is part of any whole thing. e.g. Half your pocket money. The Whole One would be all of your pocket money.

Fractions are also **Multiplications:** "Of " means Multiply.

$$--- \text{ of } --- \quad \text{or} \quad --- \times ---$$
$$\dfrac{1}{2} \qquad\qquad \dfrac{1}{2}$$

⬇

This is half of a whole, or $\frac{1}{2} \times 1$

Fractions are also **Divisions:** "Into" means Divide.

$$--- \text{ into } --- \quad \text{or} \quad --- \div ---$$
$$\dfrac{1}{2} \qquad\qquad \dfrac{1}{2}$$

⬆

Fractions Comparison Chart

The larger the Denominator of a Fraction, the smaller its value. e.g. $\frac{1}{8}$ is smaller than $\frac{1}{5}$ because it has been split into more parts.

One whole						
Half ½			**½**			
Third ⅓			⅓			
Quarter ¼		¼		¼		
Fifth $\frac{1}{5}$		$\frac{1}{5}$		$\frac{1}{5}$		$\frac{1}{5}$
Sixth $\frac{1}{6}$	$\frac{1}{6}$		$\frac{1}{6}$		$\frac{1}{6}$	$\frac{1}{6}$
Eighth $\frac{1}{8}$	$\frac{1}{8}$	$\frac{1}{8}$	$\frac{1}{8}$	$\frac{1}{8}$	$\frac{1}{8}$	$\frac{1}{8}$

2. A Fraction as a Division

All Fractions are Divisions. Therefore the Line in the middle of a Fraction simply means 'DIVIDED BY'.

Example 1: | Show **2** parts Divided by **3** diagrammatically.

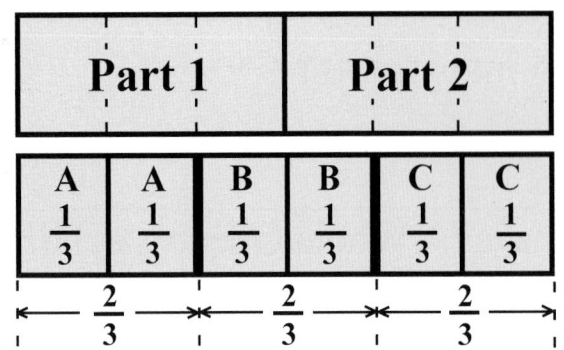

When the two parts are Divided by **3**, each new part will be two thirds.

$$2 \div 3 = \frac{2}{3}$$

Numerator - How many of each type (As, Bs etc)?

Denominator - How many groups of each type (As, Bs etc)?

– –

Example 2:

| Show **7** Divided by **8** as a Fraction.

7 Divided by 8 written as a Fraction is:

$$\frac{7}{8}$$

(Seven parts)
of
(Eight parts)

Exercise 4: 1   Write as Fractions:

Numerator - Count how many of each type - As, Bs, C's and D's etc.
Denominator - Count how many groupings there are in total.

1) If these **3** squares were Divided into **4** equal parts, each new part could be written as the Fraction ....

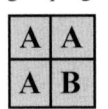 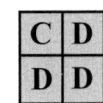

2) **4** Circles were Divided into **9** equal parts. Each new part is

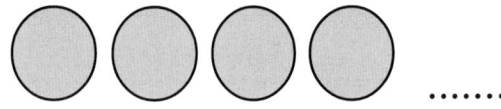

....

3) **8** Divided by **3** ....

4) **9** Divided by **10** ....

5) **5** Divided by **7** ....

– –

Write as Divisions:

6) $\dfrac{6}{7}$ ....

7) $\dfrac{4}{5}$ ....

8) $\dfrac{2}{9}$ ....

9) $\dfrac{1}{6}$ ....

10) $\dfrac{2}{5}$ ....

Score Out of Ten $\longrightarrow$

3. A Whole One as a Fraction

Whole Ones or Units can also be expressed as **Fractions**. If the Numerator and the Denominator are the same, the Fraction is equal to one Whole One.

Example: | Show Whole Ones as Fractions. |

Numerator - How many parts?
Denominator - What type of parts?

$$\frac{2}{2} = 1 \qquad \frac{3}{3} = 1 \qquad \frac{4}{4} = 1$$

Two halves make a Whole One;
Three thirds make a Whole One;
Four quarters make a Whole One.

Exercise 4: 2 Express these Whole Ones as Fractions:

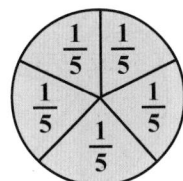 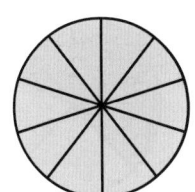 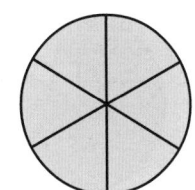 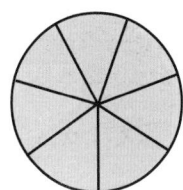

1) _____   2) _____   3) _____   4) _____

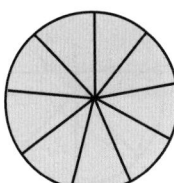 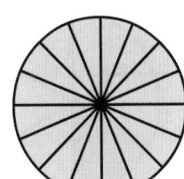 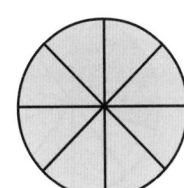 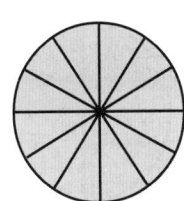

5) _____   6) _____   7) _____   8) _____

Express these Fractions as Whole Ones:

9) $\frac{15}{15}$ = _____   10) $\frac{20}{20}$ = _____   Score ☐

5

$$5) \quad \frac{36}{42} \begin{array}{c} \div \;\underline{} \\ \div \;\underline{} \end{array} = \frac{6}{7}$$

$$6) \quad \frac{5}{8} \begin{array}{c} \times \;\underline{} \\ \times \;\underline{} \end{array} = \frac{20}{32}$$

$$7) \quad \frac{72}{84} \begin{array}{c} \div \;\underline{} \\ \div \;\underline{} \end{array} = \frac{6}{7}$$

$$8) \quad \frac{3}{18} \begin{array}{c} \div \;\underline{} \\ \div \;\underline{} \end{array} = \frac{1}{6}$$

$$9) \quad \frac{8}{10} \begin{array}{c} \times \;\underline{} \\ \times \;\underline{} \end{array} = \frac{72}{90}$$

$$10) \quad \frac{1}{3} \begin{array}{c} \times \;\underline{} \\ \times \;\underline{} \end{array} = \frac{25}{75}$$

Score [ ]

6. Simple Fractions

Simple Fractions are Fractions in their **'Lowest Terms'**.

Example: | Show a Fraction in its Lowest Terms. | $\frac{1}{2}$ | This Fraction cannot be Expressed in any Lower Terms.

Simplifying Fractions into their Lowest Terms.
Find a number (Factor) that Divides into the top and bottom of the Fraction exactly with no Remainder.

$\longrightarrow$ Divide by 4

$$\frac{12}{16} \begin{array}{c} \div \; 4 \; = \; \frac{3}{4} \\ \div \; 4 \; = \end{array}$$

Simplifying is usually shown like this.

$\longrightarrow$

$$\frac{\cancel{12}^{3}}{\cancel{16}^{4}} = \frac{3}{4}$$

Dividing by Two
If the top and bottom of the Fraction are both <u>even</u> it can be Divided by two.

Example: | Simplify $\frac{16}{18}$

$$\frac{16}{18} = \begin{array}{c} \xrightarrow{\div 2} \\ \xrightarrow{\div 2} \end{array} \frac{\cancel{16}^{8}}{\cancel{18}^{9}} = \frac{8}{9}$$

Dividing by 10
If the top and bottom of the Fraction both end in **0**, it can be Divided by 10 by simply removing the **0**s on the end.

Example: | Simplify $\frac{20}{30}$

$$\frac{20}{30} = \begin{array}{c} \xrightarrow{\div 10} \\ \xrightarrow{\div 10} \end{array} \frac{\cancel{20}^{2}}{\cancel{30}^{3}} = \frac{2}{3}$$

Exercise 4: 7   Simplify the following: Score [ ]

1) $\dfrac{3}{9}$ = _____
$\dfrac{1}{3}$

2) $\dfrac{8}{12}$ = _____
$\dfrac{2}{6}$

3) $\dfrac{5}{30}$ = _____
$\dfrac{1}{3}$

4) $\dfrac{15}{18}$ = _____

5) $\dfrac{8}{32}$ = $\dfrac{2}{4}$ _____

6) $\dfrac{25}{75}$ = _____

7) $\dfrac{56}{72}$ = _____
4

8) $\dfrac{60}{96}$ = _____

$4 \times 8 \longrightarrow$ 9) $\dfrac{72}{84}$ = 4 _____

10) $\dfrac{72}{90}$ = _____

Find the **shaded Fraction of Equal value**.

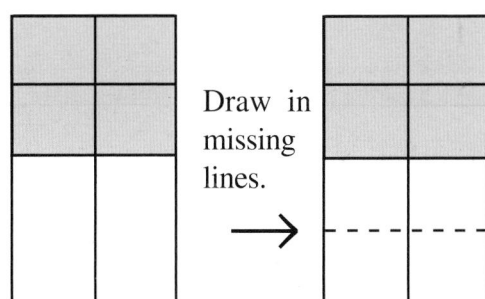

Draw in missing lines. $\longrightarrow$

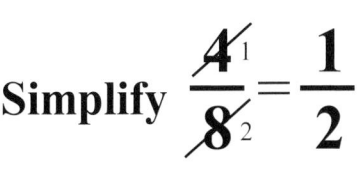

The Fraction is $\dfrac{4}{8}$

Simplify $\dfrac{\cancel{4}^{1}}{\cancel{8}_{2}} = \dfrac{1}{2}$

Divide by 4.

Exercise 4: 8   Write the Fraction in Lowest Terms:

1) 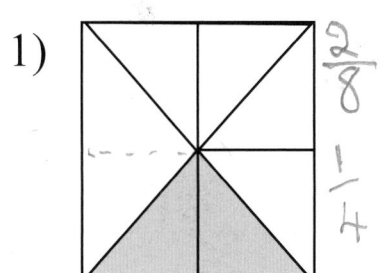 $\dfrac{2}{8}$ $\dfrac{1}{4}$

2)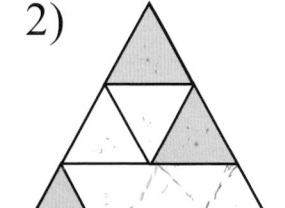

3) 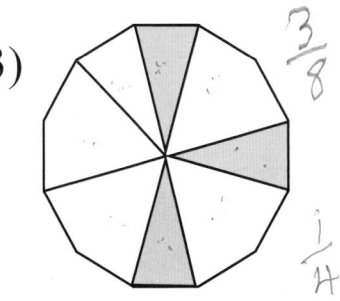 $\dfrac{3}{8}$ $\dfrac{1}{4}$

....

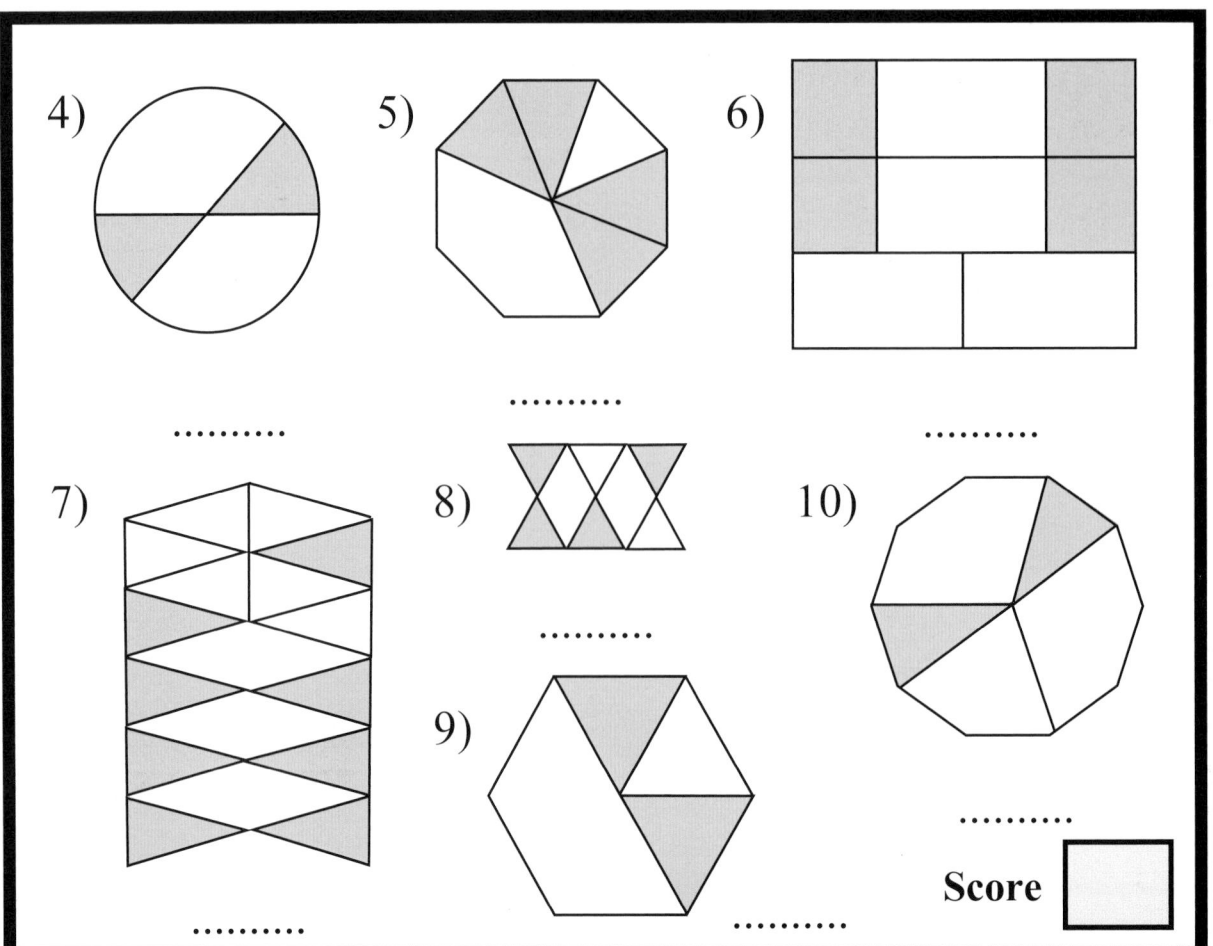

4) ....

5) ....

6) ....

7) ....

8) ....

9) ....

10) ....

Score

7. Complex Fractions

Complex Fractions are **not** in Lowest Terms.

Examples:

| Show Fractions in Complex & Simple forms. |

$$\frac{8}{16} = \frac{4}{8} = \frac{2}{4} = \frac{1}{2}$$

Complex   Complex   Complex   Simple
(Lowest Terms)

Fractions can be **Complicated** by **Multiplying** to infinite number (forever) and by any combination of numbers.

$$\frac{1}{3} \times \overset{\rightarrow}{\underset{2}{2}} = \frac{2}{6} \times \overset{\rightarrow}{\underset{3}{3}} = \frac{6}{18} \times \overset{\rightarrow}{\underset{4}{4}} = \frac{24}{72}$$

Multiply by 2   Multiply by 3   Multiply by 4

Questions often appear with a missing number.

Example:

The Multiplier is **2**.

Write in the missing number.	$\dfrac{3}{4} = \dfrac{?}{8}$

$$\dfrac{3 \times 2}{4 \times 2} = \dfrac{6}{8}$$

Exercise 4: 9 Find the missing number: **Score** ☐

1) $\dfrac{2}{3} = \dfrac{}{9}$

2) $\dfrac{1}{2} = \dfrac{6}{}$

3) $\dfrac{}{5} = \dfrac{16}{20}$

4) $\dfrac{5}{8} = \dfrac{}{24}$

5) $\dfrac{1}{3} = \dfrac{6}{}$

6) $\dfrac{}{15} = \dfrac{44}{60}$

7) $\dfrac{3}{4} = \dfrac{15}{}$

8) $\dfrac{3}{5} = \dfrac{}{30}$

9) $\dfrac{5}{} = \dfrac{15}{18}$

10) $\dfrac{7}{8} = \dfrac{}{40}$

---

8. Improper Fractions

Improper Fractions have a value of more than one unit.

An Improper Fraction has a larger Numerator and a smaller Denominator. It is '**top heavy**'.

Example:

Show seven quarters as an Improper Fraction.	$\dfrac{7}{4}$ Larger Numerator
	Smaller Denominator

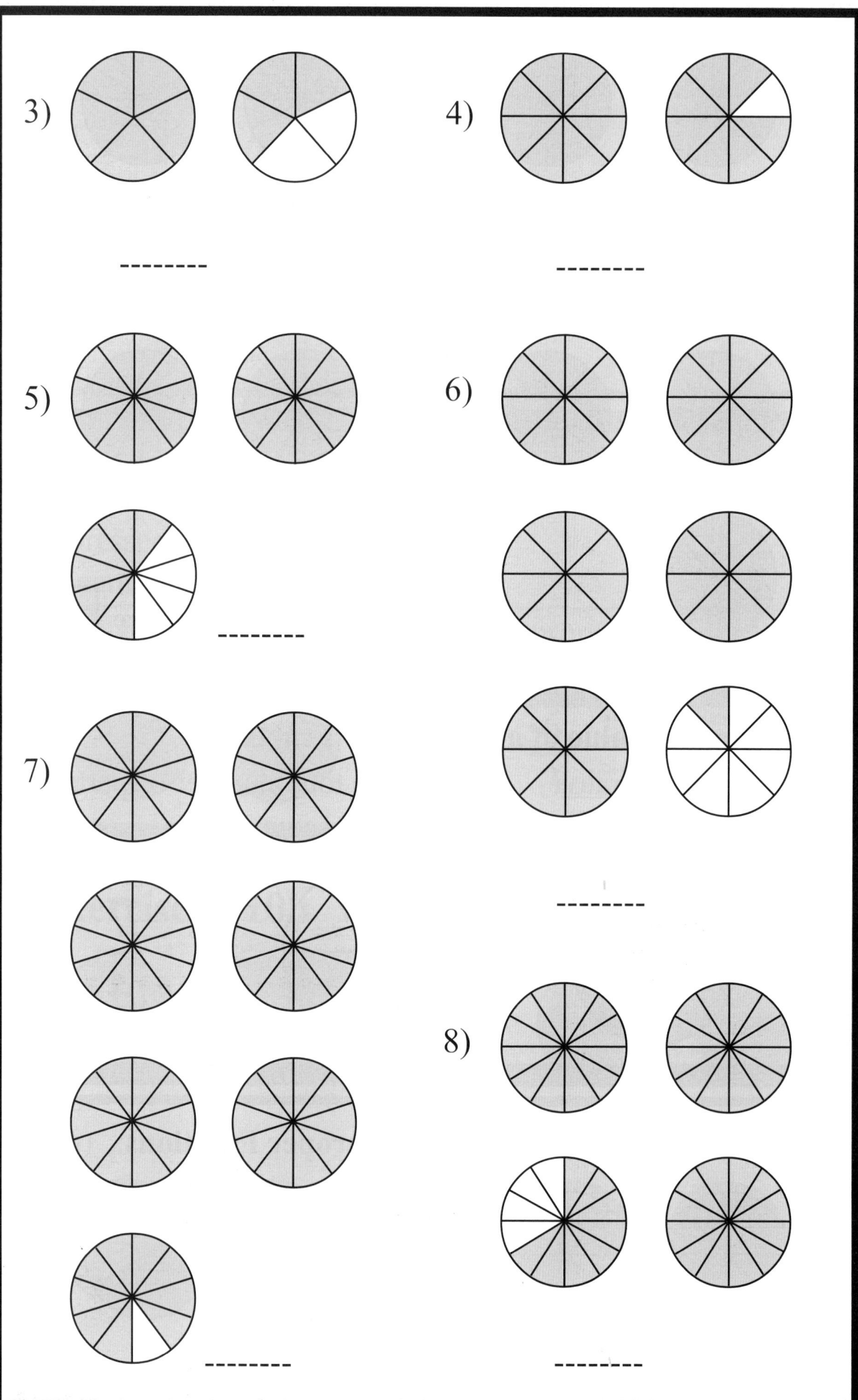

3) --------

4) --------

5) --------

6) --------

7) --------

8) --------

16

© 2006 Stephen Curran

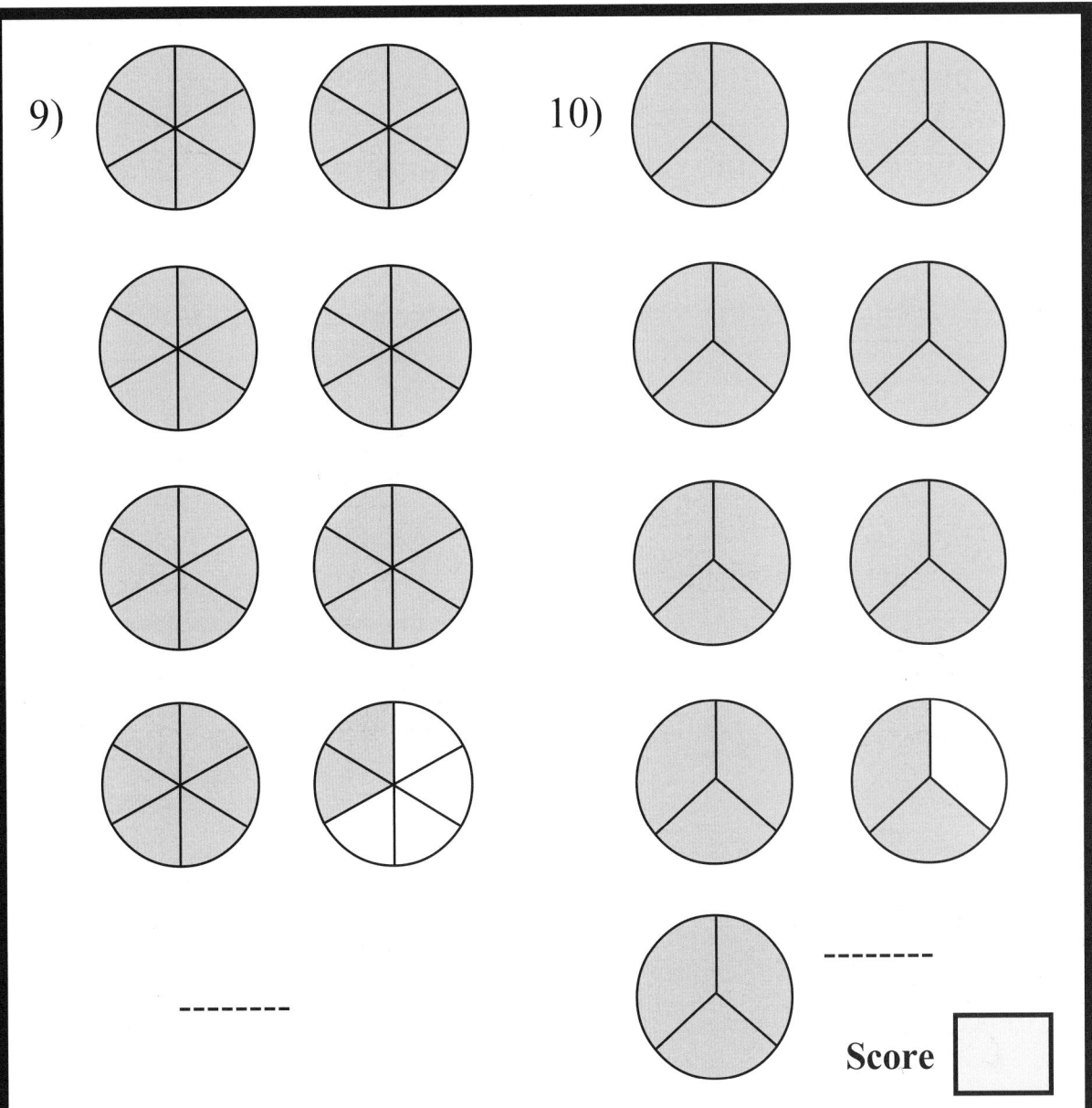

9)

10)

- - - - - - - -

- - - - - - - -

Score

9. Mixed Numbers

Mixed Numbers are Whole Numbers and Fractions combined together. The Whole Number is written first followed by the Fraction.

A Whole Number + a Fraction = a Mixed Number.

Example: | Show one and three quarters as a Mixed Number.

$$1\frac{3}{4}$$

One whole one   Three quarters

Example: Find the **Value** of this **Mixed Number**.

One whole one   +   three quarters

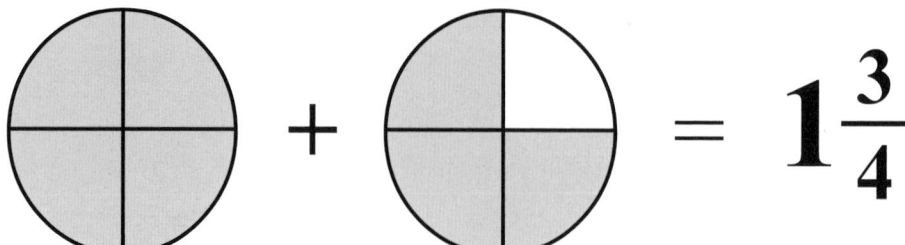

$= 1\dfrac{3}{4}$

Mixed Numbers are determined by:
- Counting the number of Whole Ones.
- Expressing the parts left over as a Fraction.

Exercise 4: 12   Write the value as a **Mixed Number**:

1)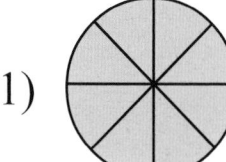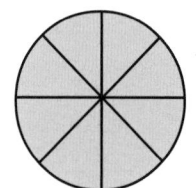

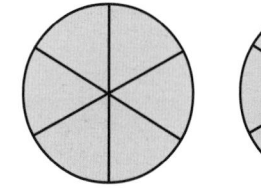 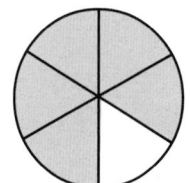

$2\dfrac{3}{8}$

2)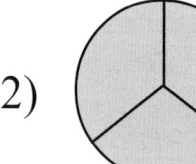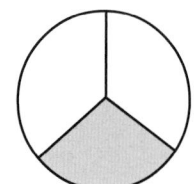

$1\dfrac{1}{3}$

3)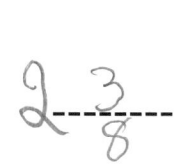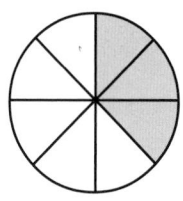

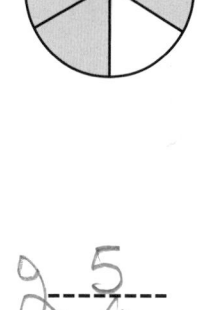

$2\dfrac{5}{6}$

4)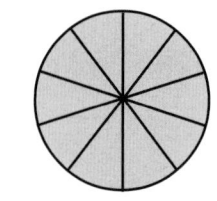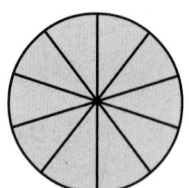

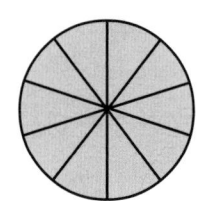 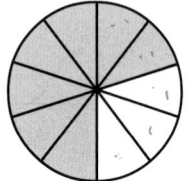

$3\dfrac{7}{10}$

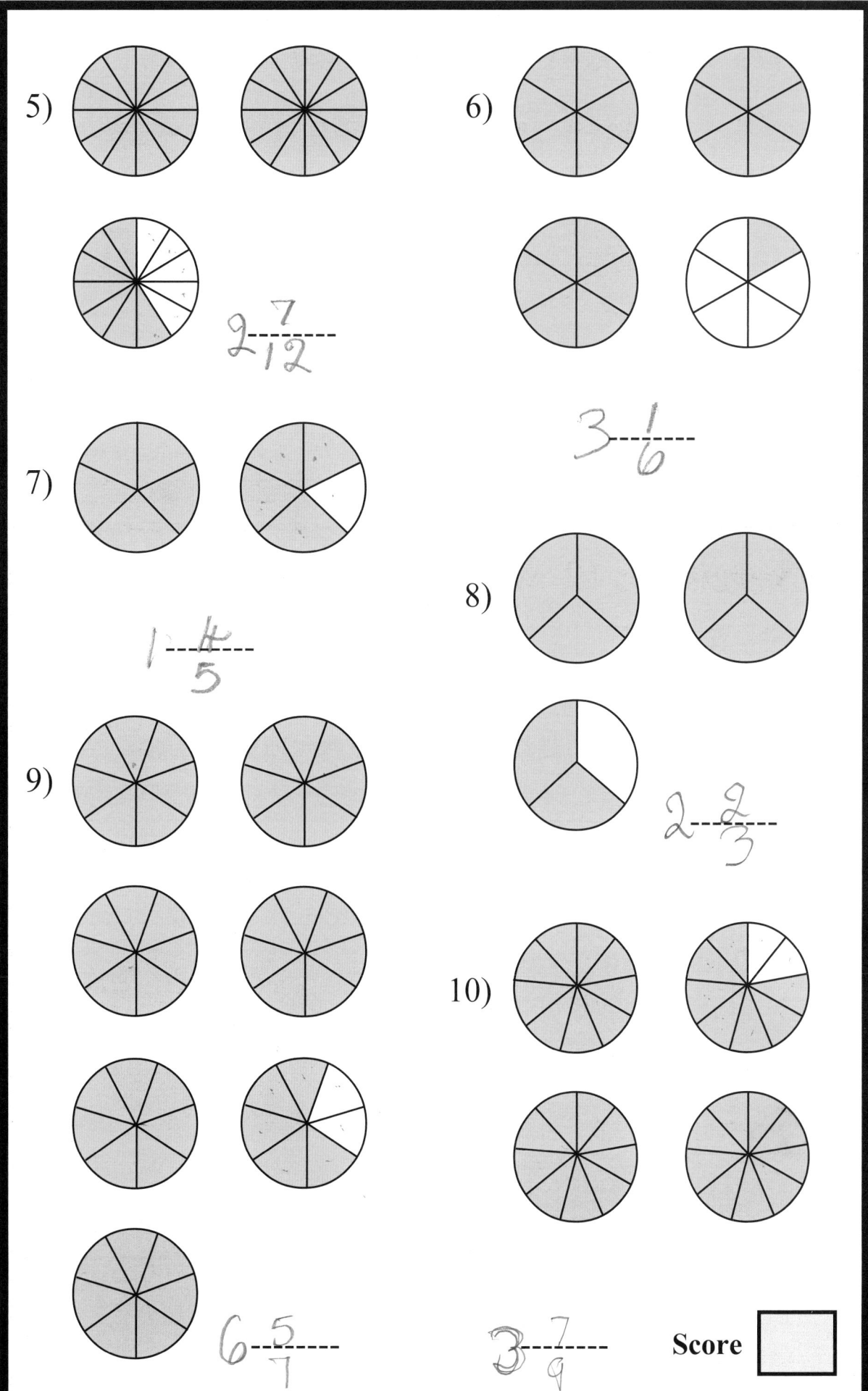

5) $2\dfrac{7}{12}$

6) $3\dfrac{1}{6}$

7) $1\dfrac{4}{5}$

8) $2\dfrac{2}{3}$

9) $6\dfrac{5}{7}$

10) $3\dfrac{7}{9}$

Score ☐

10. Mixed Numbers and Improper Fractions

Fractions can either be expressed as **Mixed Numbers** or **Improper Fractions**.

Example:

Express as a Mixed Number and an Improper Fraction.

Mixed Number   Improper Fraction

$$\bigcirc + \bigcirc = 1\frac{3}{4} \text{ or } \frac{7}{4}$$

Answers to problems are usually given in Mixed Numbers, but calculations are often done with Improper Fractions first.

a. Mixed Numbers to Improper Fractions

Example: Change $1\frac{3}{4}$ to an Improper Fraction.

To find the **Numerator** Multiply the bottom by the whole number then add the top to it.

$$1 \times 4 = 4 \quad 4 + 3 = 7$$

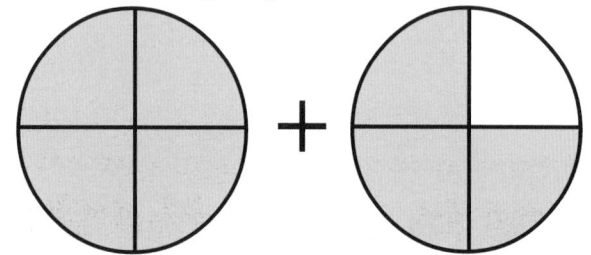

The **Denominator** remains the same.

It will $= 4$ as the Fraction is in quarters.

Numerator $\dfrac{7}{4}$ **Denominator**

Exercise 4: 13 Change to Improper Fractions:

1) $2\frac{1}{2}$ ......$\frac{3}{4}$......

2) $5\frac{3}{4}$ ....

3) $3\frac{2}{9}$ ....

4) $4\frac{2}{3}$ ....

5) $4\frac{3}{7}$ ....

6) $1\frac{5}{6}$ ....

7) $9\frac{5}{8}$ ....

8) $6\frac{4}{5}$ ....

9) $10\frac{5}{9}$ ....

10) $8\frac{7}{10}$ ....

Score ☐

b. Improper Fractions to Mixed Numbers

Example: | Change $\frac{7}{4}$ to a Mixed Number.

For the **Whole Number**:
Divide the top by the bottom.
$7 \div 4 = $ **1** whole one

For the **Fraction**:
Take the Remainder of **3** and
put it over the same Denominator
of **4** to make the Fraction of:

$\frac{3}{4}$ **three quarters**

$\frac{7}{4}$ ↑ **Divide**

$1\frac{3}{4}$

Exercise 4: 14   Change to Mixed Numbers:

1) $\frac{4}{3}$ ....

2) $\frac{5}{2}$ ....

3) $\frac{7}{6}$ ....

2. Change all the Fractions to twelfths by Multiplying the top and bottom of each Fraction.

$$\frac{2}{3} \times \frac{4}{4} = \frac{8}{12}$$

$$\frac{3}{4} \times \frac{3}{3} = \frac{9}{12}$$

3. Draw a line and make **12** the Denominator.

$$\frac{8+9}{12}$$

4. Add the Numerators (Not the Denominator).

$$\frac{17}{12}$$

5. Divide to convert the Improper Fraction to a Mixed Number.

$$1\frac{5}{12}$$

Exercise 4: 16b Add the Fractions:

6) $\frac{1}{6} + \frac{3}{5}$ 7) $\frac{5}{12} + \frac{1}{4}$ 8) $\frac{5}{9} + \frac{1}{3}$

= ....   = ...   = ...

9) $\frac{3}{4} + \frac{4}{5} + \frac{7}{10}$ 10) $\frac{4}{7} + \frac{5}{6} + \frac{1}{3}$

= ....   = ...

Score ☐

c. Fractions with Mixed Numbers

Example:

$$3\frac{2}{3} + 2\frac{3}{4}$$

1. Add the **Whole Numbers**.

2. Find the **Lowest Common Multiple** of both Denominators.

3 - 3, 6, 9, <u>12</u>

4 - 4, 8, <u>12</u>   The LCM is **12**

$$5\frac{2}{3} \; + \; \frac{3}{4}$$

$$5 \; \frac{8 + 9}{12}$$

A quick way to find the <u>new Denominator</u> - Multiply the two existing Denominators. ($3 \times 4 = \mathbf{12}$)

Make **12** the new **Denominator**.

3. To find the new **Numerators**, do the **Calculations** shown.

$$12 \div 3 = 4 \qquad 4 \times 2 = \mathbf{8}$$
$$12 \div 4 = 3 \qquad 3 \times 3 = \mathbf{9}$$

An **alternative calculation** can be done that achieves the same result. Use the Multipliers to make twelfths.	Multiply each Fraction to make twelfths. $\dfrac{2}{3} \times \dfrac{4}{4} = \dfrac{\mathbf{8}}{\mathbf{12}} \qquad \dfrac{3}{4} \times \dfrac{3}{3} = \dfrac{\mathbf{9}}{\mathbf{12}}$

$$5\frac{8 + 9}{12}$$

$$5\frac{17}{12} \uparrow \text{ Divide}$$

$$5 + 1\frac{5}{12}$$

$$6\frac{5}{12}$$

4. Add the **Numerators**.
   $8 + 9 = \mathbf{17}$

5. This is an **Improper Fraction**. Convert to a **Mixed Number**.
   $17 \div 12 = 1$ whole one and 5 twelfths left over. $\quad 1\frac{5}{12}$

6. Add the **Whole Numbers**.

7. Does the Fraction **Simplify**? No number will Divide into 5 and 12.

Exercise 4: 17   Add the following Fractions:

1) $\quad 2\frac{1}{2} + 3\frac{2}{3}$ 2) $\quad 4\frac{1}{3} + 5\frac{3}{4}$

= ....   = ...

c. Fractions with Mixed Numbers

Use the following method to Add Mixed Numbers.

Example 1:

$$5\dfrac{1}{2} \;-\; 2\dfrac{1}{3}$$

$$3\,\dfrac{1}{2} \;\;{\times}\;\; \dfrac{1}{3}$$

$$3\;\dfrac{3\;-\;2}{\div\;\;6\;\;\div}$$

$$3\;\dfrac{3\;-\;2}{6}$$

$$3\dfrac{1}{6}$$

1. Subtract the **Whole Numbers**.

2. Find the **LCM** of **2** and **3**.

   2 - 2, 4, <u>6</u>
   3 - 3, <u>6</u>   The LCM is <u>6</u>

3. **Calculation**.

   $6 \div 2 = 3$ $3 \times 1 = \mathbf{3}$
   $6 \div 3 = 2$ $2 \times 1 = \mathbf{2}$

4. Subtract the **Numerators**.

5. Is it **Improper** and will it **Simplify?** Not in this case.

Exercise 4: 19a   Subtract the following Fractions:

1) $5\dfrac{1}{2} \;-\; 1\dfrac{2}{5}$ 2) $4\dfrac{3}{4} \;-\; 1\dfrac{5}{8}$

     = ...   = ...

3) $3\frac{2}{5} - 1\frac{1}{8}$

4) $6\frac{2}{3} - 3\frac{2}{5} - \frac{1}{10}$

= ....

= ....

5) $8\frac{3}{4} - 6\frac{1}{3} - \frac{1}{6}$

6) $6\frac{3}{4} - 2\frac{3}{8}$

= ....

= ....

d. Subtractions with Borrowing

In this example the first Mixed Number is of greater value than the second Mixed Number so they can be Subtracted.

Example 2:

$$3\frac{1}{5} - 1\frac{3}{4}$$

Smaller Fraction

Bigger Fraction

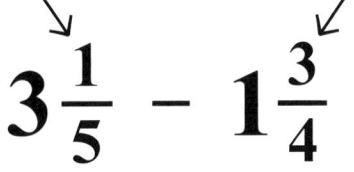

$$1\cancel{2}^{20+}\frac{4-15}{20}$$

However, the second Fraction is bigger than the first so **Borrowing** will be required.

1. Subtract the **Whole Numbers**.

2. Find the **LCM**.

3. Do the **Calculation**.

4. **Borrow** a whole one.

    $4 - 15$ cannot be done.

    Cross out the 2 and put 1.

    The whole one = $\frac{20}{20}$ and is put into the Fraction.

3) $1\frac{1}{2} \times 7$

= ....

4) $2\frac{1}{2} \times 2\frac{2}{5}$

= ....

5) $\frac{3}{5} \times \frac{2}{3}$

= ....

6) $\frac{3}{8} \times 56$

= ....

7) $5\frac{1}{2} \times \frac{3}{8}$

= ....

8) $4\frac{2}{5} \times \frac{5}{11}$

= ....

9) $\frac{8}{11} \times 1\frac{1}{3}$

= ....

10) $\frac{1}{8} \times 1\frac{3}{5}$

= ....

Score

17. Dividing Fractions
a. Proper Fractions

Dividing Proper Fractions involves two extra stages:

Example: $\dfrac{7}{8} \div \dfrac{7}{16}$

1. The 2nd Fraction is Inverted
2. The Division sign is changed to Multiplication.

$$\frac{7}{16} \xrightarrow{\text{Invert}} \frac{16}{7}$$

1. Turn the 2nd Fraction (the Divisor) upside down (Invert).

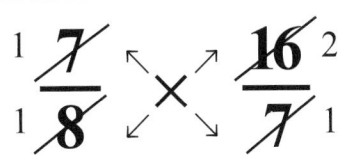

2. Change the Division Sign to a Multiplication Sign.

$$\frac{7}{8} \div \frac{7}{16} \longrightarrow \frac{7}{8} \times \frac{16}{7}$$

$$\frac{1}{1} \xrightarrow{\times} \frac{2}{1}$$

3. Cancel the Fractions as normal.
4. Multiply out the Fractions.

$$\frac{2}{1} \uparrow_{\text{Divide}} = 2$$

5. Is it an Improper Fraction? Yes
6. Will it Simplify? No.

Exercise 4: 23 Divide the following Fractions:

1) $\dfrac{3}{4} \div \dfrac{1}{2}$ 2) $\dfrac{5}{6} \div \dfrac{2}{3}$ 3) $\dfrac{2}{5} \div \dfrac{4}{5}$

$= \dots\dots$ $= \dots\dots$ $= \dots\dots$

4) $\dfrac{3}{4} \div \dfrac{6}{8}$ 5) $\dfrac{5}{6} \div \dfrac{10}{12}$ 6) $\dfrac{3}{5} \div \dfrac{9}{10}$

$= \dots\dots$ $= \dots\dots$ $= \dots\dots$

7) $\dfrac{6}{7} \div \dfrac{15}{21}$ 8) $\dfrac{8}{9} \div \dfrac{2}{3}$ 9) $\dfrac{5}{12} \div \dfrac{5}{6}$

$= \dots\dots$ $= \dots\dots$ $= \dots\dots$

10) $\dfrac{4}{5} \div \dfrac{16}{25}$

$= \dots\dots$ **Score**

b. Mixed Numbers

Method (Same as Multiplying except for stage 2).

Example: $\boxed{2\dfrac{1}{4} \div 1\dfrac{7}{8} \longrightarrow \begin{array}{c} \text{This is exactly} \\ \text{the same sum.} \end{array} \dfrac{2\dfrac{1}{4}}{1\dfrac{7}{8}} \begin{array}{l} \text{If the sum is} \\ \text{given in this} \\ \text{format, set it} \\ \text{out in the} \\ \text{original way.} \end{array}}$

1. **Convert to Improper Fractions.**

$$\dfrac{9}{4} \nearrow \div \dfrac{15}{8}$$

Change to ×   Invert
the 2nd
Fraction

2. **Three Rules of Division.**
   a. Turn the 2nd Fraction upside down (Invert). This is called the **Reciprocal** of the original Fraction.
   b. Change the Division sign to a Multiply sign.
   c. Proceed as a normal Multiplication.

$$\dfrac{\overset{3}{\cancel{9}}}{\underset{1}{\cancel{4}}} \times \dfrac{\overset{2}{\cancel{8}}}{\underset{5}{\cancel{15}}}$$

3. **Cancel** (cross-divide).

$$\dfrac{3}{1} \times \dfrac{2}{5}$$

4. **Multiply out the Fractions.**

$$\dfrac{6}{5} \uparrow \text{ Divide}$$

5. Is it an **Improper Fraction?** Yes, so Divide the Fraction.

$$1\dfrac{1}{5}$$

6. Will it **Simplify?** The Fraction is already in Lowest Terms.

Exercise 4: 24   Divide the following Fractions:

1) $3\dfrac{1}{5} \div 1\dfrac{7}{25}$ 2) $3\dfrac{1}{3} \div 1\dfrac{2}{3}$

= ....   = ...

3) $1\frac{1}{2} \div 3$

4) $\frac{5}{8} \div 1\frac{2}{3}$

= ....

= ....

5) $3\frac{1}{2} \div 1\frac{1}{4}$

6) $7\frac{1}{2} \div 3$

= ....

= ....

7) $5\frac{1}{2} \div \frac{4}{5}$

8) $\frac{3}{4} \div \frac{1}{5}$

= ....

= ....

9) $\dfrac{1\frac{1}{2}}{\frac{2}{3}}$ This question should be set out like this before commencing.

$1\frac{1}{2} \div \frac{2}{3}$

10) $\dfrac{2\frac{2}{9}}{1\frac{2}{3}}$

Score

= ....

= ....

18. Two Rule Fractions (× & ÷)

Some Fraction sums involve Multiplication and Division.
Example:

Solve the following:

$\frac{2}{3} \times \frac{5}{8} \div \frac{5}{9}$

→ The same sum can be written like this without the Brackets.

$\dfrac{\frac{2}{3} \times \frac{5}{8}}{\frac{5}{9}}$

Exercise 4: 25   Calculate the following: Score

1) $1\frac{1}{3} \div 2 \div \frac{7}{15}$ = ...

2) $\dfrac{3\frac{9}{10} \div 6\frac{1}{2}}{\frac{7}{15}}$ = ...

3) $5\frac{1}{2} \times \frac{9}{10} \div 4\frac{2}{5}$ = ...

4) $1\frac{2}{3} \times \frac{7}{10} \div 2\frac{4}{5}$ = ...

5) $\dfrac{3\frac{1}{3} \times \frac{4}{5}}{5\frac{1}{3}}$ = ...

6) $2\frac{2}{3} \times \frac{1}{2} \div 1\frac{3}{5}$ = ...

7) $\frac{3}{8} \times \frac{3}{8} \times \frac{4}{9}$ = ...

8) $1\frac{5}{6} \times \frac{3}{5} \div 8\frac{1}{4}$ = ...

9) $2\frac{1}{2} \div 1\frac{1}{3} \div 2\frac{1}{12}$ = ...

10) $\frac{1}{4} \times \frac{2}{3} \div \frac{5}{9}$ = ...

19. Four Rule Fractions (+ − × ÷)

The **B I D M A S** acronym gives the Order of Operations.

Brackets, **I**ndices, **D**ivision, **M**ultiplication, **A**ddition and **S**ubtraction

Do the Brackets first, then do ÷ or ×, then do + or − .

a. With Brackets

If there are Brackets, always do the sums inside first.
Example:

Show the Order of Operations in:

$3\frac{2}{5} \div \left(2\frac{1}{2} + \frac{1}{3}\right)$ → The same sum can be written like this without the Brackets. $\dfrac{3\frac{2}{5}}{2\frac{1}{2} + \frac{1}{3}}$

Operation 1	Operation 2
Add $\quad 2\frac{1}{2} + \frac{1}{3} = 2\frac{5}{6}$	Divide $\quad 3\frac{2}{5} \div 2\frac{5}{6} = 1\frac{1}{5}$

Exercise 4: 26a   Calculate the following:

1) $5\frac{5}{6} \div (3\frac{1}{2} + \frac{2}{3}) =$ ....

2) $\dfrac{\frac{1}{4} + \frac{1}{7}}{3\frac{3}{10}} =$ ....

3) $\dfrac{2\frac{4}{5} \div 2\frac{1}{2}}{1\frac{2}{5} \times \frac{1}{3}} =$ ....

4) $1\frac{4}{5} \times (2\frac{1}{4} - \frac{7}{12}) =$ ....

5) $(4\frac{1}{2} - 1\frac{3}{4}) \div 7\frac{1}{3} =$ ....

b. Without Brackets

When there are no Brackets, ensure that you do the ÷ or × sums first then do the + or − sums next.
 Example:

Show the Order of Operations in:	$2\frac{1}{4} \times 2\frac{5}{6} - 1\frac{2}{3}$

Operation 1	Operation 2
Multiply $\quad 2\frac{1}{4} \times 2\frac{5}{6} = 6\frac{3}{8}$	Subtract $\quad 6\frac{3}{8} - 1\frac{2}{3} = 4\frac{17}{24}$

Exercise 4: 26b   Calculate the following:

6) $3\frac{1}{7} \div 1\frac{3}{8} + \frac{1}{2} =$ ......

7) $\frac{1}{2} + 3\frac{3}{5} \times \frac{5}{8} =$ ....

8) $1\frac{1}{7} \times 2\frac{3}{4} \div 4 =$ ......

9) $5\frac{1}{3} \times \frac{5}{8} - 3\frac{1}{3} =$ ......

10) $4\frac{3}{4} - 1\frac{3}{10} \times 2\frac{1}{2} =$ ....

Score ☐

20. Fractional Parts

Example:

$$\boxed{\text{Find } \frac{7}{8} \text{ of } 96}$$ This sum can be done in two ways.

1. a. Find the value of $\frac{1}{8}$ Divide the Whole Number by the Denominator.
$$96 \div 8 = 12$$

   b. Find the value of $\frac{7}{8}$ Multiply by the Numerator.
$$7 \times 12 = 84$$

2. Multiplying can be termed as 'of'

$$\frac{7}{{}^1\cancel{8}} \times \frac{\cancel{96}^{\,12}}{1} = \frac{7 \times 12}{1 \times 1} = 84$$

Exercise 4: 27a   Find the Fractional Part:

1) $\frac{2}{3}$ of **387** = ...   2) $\frac{5}{7}$ of **273** = ...

3) $\frac{4}{5}$ of **540** = ...   4) $\frac{8}{11}$ of **341** = ...

5) $\frac{5}{6}$ of **240** = ...

Example:

$$\boxed{\text{Find the \textbf{whole} when: } \frac{4}{5} \text{ is 84}}$$ 2 methods again.

1. a. Divide the Whole Number by the Numerator to find how big each part is. $$84 \div 4 = 21$$

   b. Multiply the part by the Denominator to find the size of the Whole Number. $$21 \times 5 = 105$$

2. It can be done by Dividing Fractions.

('**is**' can be treated as ÷)

$$\frac{84}{1} \div \frac{4}{5} \longrightarrow \frac{{}^{21}\cancel{84}}{1} \times \frac{5}{\cancel{4}_1}$$

$$\frac{21 \times 5}{1 \times 1} = 105$$

Exercise 4: 27b   Find the whole when:

6) $\frac{4}{5}$ is **120** = ...   7) $\frac{6}{7}$ is **420** = ...

8) $\frac{5}{8}$ is **625** = ...   9) $\frac{5}{7}$ is **130** = ...

10) $\frac{9}{20}$ is **270** = ...   Score ☐

---

21. Decimals and Fractions
a. Converting Decimals to Fractions

Example: | Convert **1.375** to a Mixed Number. |

1. Draw a **Decimal Table** and place the Value in it.

U	t	h	th
1 •	3	7	5

1 whole one and 375 thousandths or $\longrightarrow 1\frac{375}{1000}$

2. **Simplify** $1\frac{\cancel{375}^{15}}{\cancel{1000}_{40}} \longrightarrow 1\frac{\cancel{15}^{3}}{\cancel{40}_8} \longrightarrow 1\frac{3}{8}$

Divide by 25.   Divide by 5.

Therefore **1.375** = $1\frac{3}{8}$

Exercise 4: 28 Change to Fractions: **Score**

1) 0.5 = ...
2) 0.125 = ...
3) 3.36 = ...
4) 4.675 = ...
5) 0.7 = ...
6) 8.15 = ...
7) 6.8 = ...
8) 3.2 = ...
9) 5.75 = ...
10) 4.625 = ...

b. Converting Fractions to Decimals

Example: Convert $1\frac{3}{8}$ to a Decimal.

The Whole Number stays the same.

Divide the Fraction $3 \div 8 = 0.375$

$$8\overline{)3.0\overset{6}{0}\overset{4}{0}} \quad 0.375$$

Therefore $1\frac{3}{8} = 1.375$

Exercise 4: 29 Change to Decimals, correct to 3 d.p.

1) $\frac{5}{8}$ = ...
2) $\frac{2}{3}$ = ...
3) $3\frac{1}{6}$ = ...
4) $3\frac{2}{5}$ = ...
5) $4\frac{1}{7}$ = ...
6) $\frac{1}{8}$ = ...
7) $3\frac{4}{9}$ = ...
8) $2\frac{7}{8}$ = ...

Score

9) $\frac{4}{7}$ = ...
10) $2\frac{4}{5}$ = ...

22. Fractions in Size Order

Method 1   **A. Change into Fractions of the same type.**

Example:

Arrange the Fractions in size order, smallest first.	$\dfrac{5}{12}$ $\dfrac{3}{4}$ $\dfrac{1}{2}$ $\dfrac{2}{3}$

1. The Denominators will all Divide into **12** (**LCD** is **12**), so make them all into twelfths by Multiplying.

Multiply by three.   Multiply by six.   Multiply by four.

$\boxed{\dfrac{5}{12}}$ $\dfrac{3}{4} \times 3 = \boxed{\dfrac{9}{12}}$ $\dfrac{1}{2} \times 6 = \boxed{\dfrac{6}{12}}$ $\dfrac{2}{3} \times 4 = \boxed{\dfrac{8}{12}}$

2. Arrange in size order.

$\dfrac{5}{12}$ $\dfrac{6}{12}$ $\dfrac{8}{12}$ $\dfrac{9}{12}$

$\downarrow$ $\downarrow$ $\downarrow$ $\downarrow$

3. Convert ordered Fractions back to original form.

$\dfrac{5}{12}$ $\dfrac{1}{2}$ $\dfrac{2}{3}$ $\dfrac{3}{4}$

Exercise 4: 30a

Make the Fractions have the same Denominator:

Which of these Fractions are **bigger?**

1) $\dfrac{5}{6}$ $\dfrac{4}{5}$ ....

2) $\dfrac{2}{3}$ $\dfrac{3}{4}$ ....

3) $\dfrac{5}{6}$ $\dfrac{6}{7}$ ....

Put in size order, **smallest first**:

4) $\dfrac{7}{8}$ $\dfrac{3}{4}$ $\dfrac{13}{16}$

5) $\dfrac{9}{20}$ $\dfrac{1}{5}$ $\dfrac{3}{10}$ $\dfrac{5}{8}$

= ....

= ....

<u>Method 2</u>   **B. Change into Decimals First**.

Example: $\dfrac{5}{12}$ $\dfrac{3}{4}$ $\dfrac{1}{2}$ $\dfrac{2}{3}$ Arrange the Fractions in size order, smallest first.

1. Change the Fractions you know into Decimals. $\dfrac{1}{2} = 0.5$ $\dfrac{3}{4} = 0.75$

2. Divide the other Fractions to obtain Decimal Values.

$\dfrac{5}{12}$ ↑ Divide $12\overline{)5.000}$ $\dfrac{0.416}{}$

$\dfrac{5}{12} = 0.42$

$\begin{array}{r} 0.416 \\ 12\overline{)5.000} \\ \underline{4\,8}\downarrow \\ 20 \\ \underline{12}\downarrow \\ 80 \end{array}$

$\dfrac{2}{3}$ ↑ Divide $3\overline{)2.00}$ $\dfrac{0.66}{}$

$\dfrac{2}{3} = 0.\dot{6}$

3. Arrange in size order.   **0.42   0.5   0.6̇   0.75**

↓   ↓   ↓   ↓

4. Convert ordered Decimals back to Fractions. $\dfrac{5}{12}$ $\dfrac{1}{2}$ $\dfrac{2}{3}$ $\dfrac{3}{4}$

Exercise 4: 30b

Score

Change the Fractions into Decimals first.

Which of these Fractions are **smaller**?

6) $\dfrac{4}{5}$ $\dfrac{3}{4}$ ....   7) $\dfrac{4}{7}$ $\dfrac{2}{3}$ ....   8) $\dfrac{3}{5}$ $\dfrac{5}{8}$ ....

Put in size order, **largest first**:

9) $\dfrac{9}{16}$ $\dfrac{3}{4}$ $\dfrac{3}{8}$ 10) $\dfrac{1}{2}$ $\dfrac{3}{5}$ $\dfrac{2}{3}$ $\dfrac{5}{6}$

= ....   = ...

Questions sometimes mix Fractions and Decimals.

If possible convert the Decimals to Fractions as this is more straightforward. When there is no **LCM** all the Fractions must be converted to Decimals as in most questions below:

Exercise 4: 31   Which is **smallest?**   Score

Convert to Fractions

1) **0.6** $\frac{3}{10}$ **0.15**   ....

Convert to Decimals

2) $\frac{7}{11}$ **0.57** $\frac{3}{8}$ ....

Convert to Fractions

3) $\frac{9}{20}$ **0.56** $\frac{3}{4}$ ....

Convert to Decimals

4) **1.1** $\frac{7}{8}$ **0.95**   ....

Which is **largest?**

Convert to Decimals

5) **0.47** $\frac{4}{9}$ **0.76**   ....

Convert to Decimals

6) **0.44** $\frac{3}{5}$ **0.53**   ....

Convert to Decimals

7) $\frac{7}{12}$ **0.61** $\frac{5}{8}$ ....

Convert to Fractions

8) $\frac{7}{10}$ **0.78** $\frac{3}{5}$ ....

Convert to Decimals in both cases.

9) Put in size order, **smallest first**.   **0.95** $\frac{5}{8}$ **0.59**   = ...

10) Put in size order, **largest first**. $\frac{1}{12}$ **0.13** $\frac{1}{9}$ = ...

23. Fraction Problems

Fractions often appear in problem solving questions.

Example:

Paul is **9$\frac{1}{2}$** years old and his grandfather is **76** years old. Express Paul's age as a Fraction of his grandfather's age.

1. Multiply **9$\frac{1}{2}$** and **76** by **2** to eliminate the Fraction.

$9\frac{1}{2} \times 2 = 19 \qquad 76 \times 2 = 152$

2. Express **19** and **152** as a Fraction and then Simplify.

$$\frac{\cancel{19}^{\,1}}{\cancel{152}^{\,8}} = \frac{1}{8}$$

Exercise 4: 32   Solve the following problems:

1) Pavneet walks **3** miles on a sponsored walk of **15** miles. What Fraction of the walk did he complete?   ....

2) John gave Priya $\frac{1}{3}$ and Navin $\frac{1}{4}$ of his birthday cake. What Fraction of the cake did that leave for John?   ....

3) Larry drank $\frac{4}{5}$ of $\frac{3}{4}$ of $\frac{5}{6}$ of his cola can. What Fraction of the cola was left? (Remember **of** is ×)   ....

4) Two identical chocolate bars were equally Divided between **3** children. What Fraction did each receive? ....

5) Alex is $1\frac{1}{2}$ times older than his sister, Philippa. If Alex is **9** years old, how old is Philippa? .... years.

6) Find the Sum of $1\frac{2}{3}$, $3\frac{4}{5}$ and $2\frac{3}{4}$. ....

7) Multiply the Sum of $5\frac{3}{10}$ and $4\frac{1}{2}$ by $1\frac{3}{7}$. ....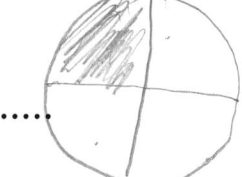

8) Divide $2\frac{5}{6}$ by the Sum of $2\frac{1}{2}$ and $\frac{1}{3}$. ....

9) Subtract $\frac{5}{6}$ from the Product of $\frac{4}{5}$ and $2\frac{7}{8}$. ....   **Score**

10) Add $3\frac{5}{6}$ to the Quotient of $1\frac{4}{7}$ and $2\frac{3}{4}$. ....

24. Fraction Boxes

Some Fraction Problems can be solved with a **Fraction Box**.

Paula is given a new reading book that has **96 pages**. She reads $\frac{3}{8}$ of the book. How many pages does she still have to read?	1. **The Missing Fraction.** This Fraction completes the whole one. $$\frac{3}{8} + \boxed{\frac{5}{8}} = \frac{8}{8}$$

Pages Read	Pages to Read
Given Fraction **$\frac{3}{8}$** (12)	Missing Fraction **$\frac{5}{8}$** (12)
Amount 3 × 12 = 36 **36**	Amount 5 × 12 = 60 **60**
Total 36 + 60 = 96 **96**	Value - One Part **$\frac{1}{8}$ = 12**

2. **The Value of One Part**.

What is one part of a total of **8** parts?

Divide 96 by the Denominator 8.

$\frac{1}{8}$ of 96 = **12**

3. **Calculate the Amounts**.

Multiply 12 by the Numerators.

3 × 12 = **36** pages

5 × 12 = **60** pages

Paula still has **60** pages to read.

For the **total number** just add the Amounts together.

Exercise 4: 33a Solve the following:

Given Fraction	Missing Fraction
Amount	Amount
Total	One Part

1) $\frac{3}{7}$ of the children on a trip are boys. **28** are girls. How many children went on the trip?
.... children.

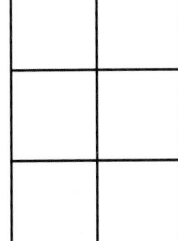

2) In a class of **27** children, $\frac{1}{3}$ of them enjoy playing computer games. How many do not enjoy the games? .... children.

3) A school brochure has **72** pages. $\frac{3}{8}$ of the pages contain photographs. How many pages do not contain any photographs? .... pages.

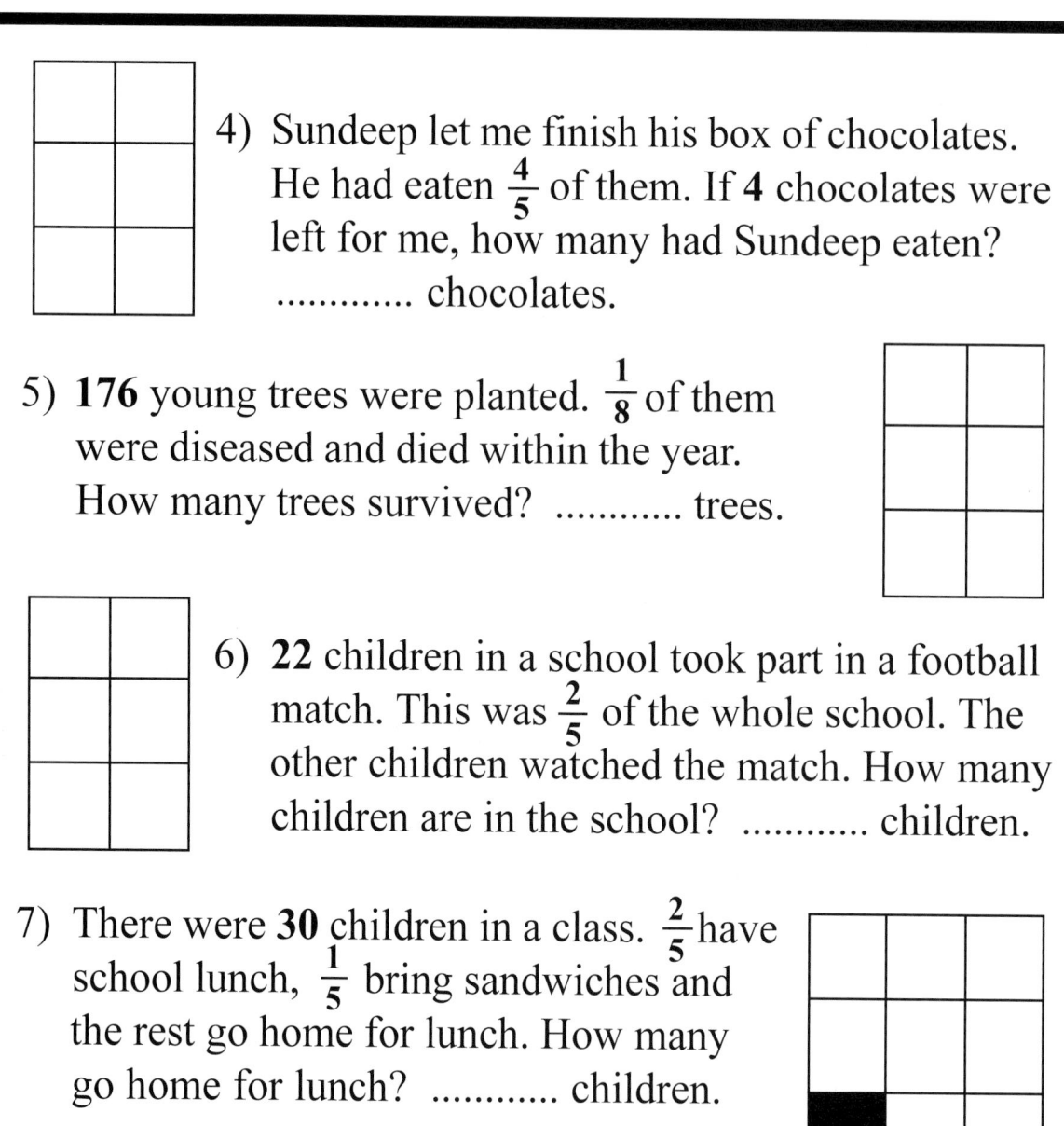

4) Sundeep let me finish his box of chocolates. He had eaten $\frac{4}{5}$ of them. If **4** chocolates were left for me, how many had Sundeep eaten? .... chocolates.

5) **176** young trees were planted. $\frac{1}{8}$ of them were diseased and died within the year. How many trees survived? .... trees.

6) **22** children in a school took part in a football match. This was $\frac{2}{5}$ of the whole school. The other children watched the match. How many children are in the school? .... children.

7) There were **30** children in a class. $\frac{2}{5}$ have school lunch, $\frac{1}{5}$ bring sandwiches and the rest go home for lunch. How many go home for lunch? .... children.

(Note - Box has only 8 pieces of information.)

Variations on the **Fraction Box** question:

Example:

Some sweets were shared out. Susan got $\frac{2}{5}$ of them. She gave **6** to Peter and had **12** left. How many sweets were there altogether?

There are two parts to this question.
1. Find the Original Amounts that people had or what they are left with.
2. Use the Fraction Box to solve the problem.

1. **Original Amounts**.

   <u>**Add**</u> 6 and 12 to find the $\frac{2}{5}$ that Susan had at first.

   <u>Susan had 18 sweets</u> originally so $\frac{2}{5}$ = **18**

2. **Fraction Box**.

Fraction given	Fraction missing
$\frac{2}{5}$	$\frac{3}{5}$
Amount 2 × 9 = **18** **18**	Amount 3 × 9 = **27** **27**
Total 18 + 27 = **45** **45**	One Part 45 ÷ 5 = **9** $\frac{1}{5}$ = **9**

a. Fill in the Missing Fraction.

   $\frac{2}{5}$ + $\boxed{\frac{3}{5}}$ = $\frac{5}{5}$

b. Find the value of One Part.

   If $\frac{2}{5}$ = 18 then $\frac{1}{5}$ = **9**

c. Calculate the Other Amount.

   3 × 9 = **27**

d. Find the Total.

   18 + 27 = **45**

   There were **45 sweets** altogether.

Given Fraction	Missing Fraction
Amount	Amount
Total	One Part

Exercise 4: 33b   Solve the following:

8) When $\frac{4}{9}$ of a certain number is reduced by **19**, the result is **21**. What is the number? The number is ....

9) When some mints were shared John received $\frac{5}{12}$ of them. He gave **6** to Sunil and had **14** left. How many mints were there altogether? .... mints.

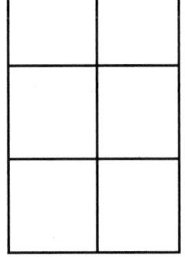

10) Peter swaps $\frac{2}{5}$ of his **35** stickers for **9** of Lucy's. How many has Peter got now?

.... stickers.

Do in this order.

1. Fraction Box.
2. Calculate what Peter is left with:

Score

25. Fraction Number Lines

Number Lines often utilise Fractions. The Fractions must be changed to the most appropriate unit for working. Example:

> Write in $\frac{13}{32}$ and its Decimal Value on the Number Line.

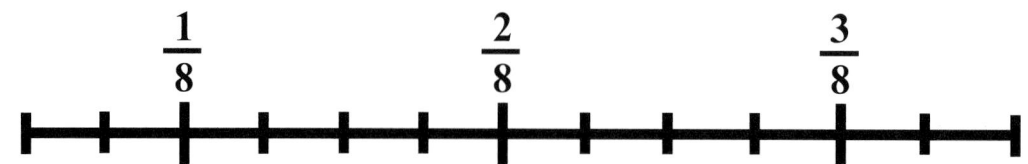

$$\frac{1}{8} \qquad\qquad \frac{2}{8} \qquad\qquad \frac{3}{8}$$

1. Convert the given Fractions to 32nds (multiply by 4).

2. Place $\frac{13}{32}$ on the Number Line (Line units are 32nds).

3. Divide the Fraction to find a Decimal $13 \div 32 \approx 0.41$

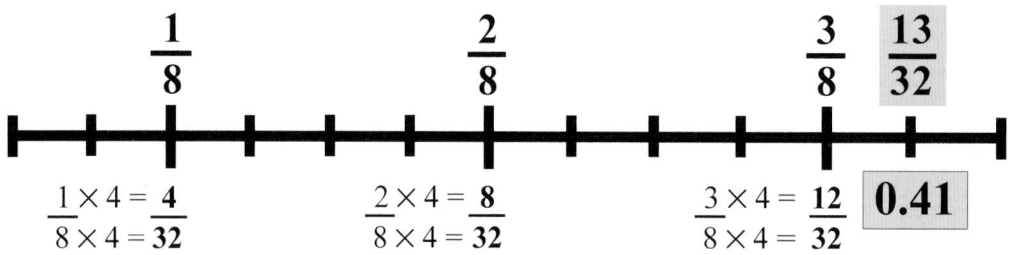

$$\frac{1}{8} \qquad\qquad \frac{2}{8} \qquad\qquad \frac{3}{8} \quad \boxed{\frac{13}{32}}$$

$$\frac{1\times4=4}{8\times4=32} \qquad \frac{2\times4=8}{8\times4=32} \qquad \frac{3\times4=12}{8\times4=32} \quad \boxed{0.41}$$

Exercise 4: 34 Calculate the following: Score ☐

Write as Fractions.

0   1) ☐   2) ☐   3) ☐ $\frac{1}{2}$

Write as Decimals. 4) ☐   5) ☐

- -

6) ☐ $\frac{3}{5}$ 7) ☐ $\frac{4}{5}$ 8) ☐

9) ☐   10) ☐

26. More Fraction Problems

Exercise 4: 35   Answer the following: Score [   ]

1) How much would each child get if six and a half cakes were shared among four children? (Divide) .... cakes.

2) What is three quarters of four ninths? .... (Multiply)

3) Subtract $11\frac{1}{6} - 3\frac{3}{7}$

= ....

4) Add $4\frac{5}{8} + 5\frac{9}{16}$

= ....

5) Divide $4\frac{2}{3} \div 5\frac{4}{9}$

= ....

6) Multiply $4\frac{1}{8} \times 7\frac{3}{11}$

= ....

7) A boy scored **66** points on the first stage of a computer game. This was $\frac{3}{5}$ of his final score. What was his score once he had completed the game? ....

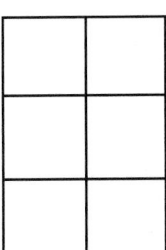

8) Simplify the following Fractions:

a) $\frac{60}{96}$ ......

b) $\frac{14}{70}$ ......

c) $\frac{21}{56}$ ......

9) Convert these Improper Fractions into Mixed Numbers:

a) $\frac{72}{50}$ ....

b) $\frac{24}{10}$ ....

c) $\frac{50}{16}$ ....

10) Convert these Mixed Numbers into Improper Fractions:

a) $6\frac{8}{9}$ ....

b) $3\frac{6}{7}$ ....

c) $2\frac{9}{10}$ ....

Chapter Five
MONEY AND COSTS
1. Units of Currency

Most money systems (currencies) in the world are based on the tens number system (units of ten).
- The United Kingdom uses Pounds and Pence.
  There are a hundred Pence to one Pound.
- Countries in the European Union (including the UK) use the Euro (€) and Cent as a unit of currency. There are one hundred Cent to the Euro.
- The USA uses Dollars ($) and Cents.
  There are one hundred Cents to the Dollar.

2. Pounds and Pence

Multiply by 100 to change **Pounds to Pence**.   Example:
(Move Decimal Point 2 places to the right.)   £1.63 = 163p

Divide by 100 to change **Pence to Pounds**.   Example:
(Move Decimal Point 2 places to the left.)   953p = £9.53

Exercise 5: 1   Score

Change to Pence: Change to Pounds:

1) **£6.30** = ...   6) **76p** = ...

2) **£0.41** = ...   7) **1540p** = ...

3) **£8.95** = ...   8) **153p** = ...

4) **£5.69** = ...   9) **7p**   = ...

5) **£9.02** = ...   10) **18p**   = ...

3. Money Calculations

Exercise 5: 2   Set out and calculate: Score [   ]

1) **£3.44 + 69p + £7.56**
   = £ ....

2) **£7.84 − 97p**
   = £ ....

3) **599p + £ 4.37 + £0.88**
   = £ ....

4) **£8.07 − 596p**
   = £ ....

5) **67 × £5.32**   = £ ....

6) **56 × 730p** = £ ....

7) **£7.70 ÷ 1.4**   = £ ....

8) **656p ÷ 16** = £ ....

9) **£66.73 × 9**   = £ ....

10) **£78.8 ÷ 8** = £ ....

4. Money Problems

Money problems make use of the **Four Rules of Decimals**.
Example:

Peter is given **£7.50** at Christmas and a further **£12.50** on his birthday from his aunt. His younger brother Jonathan receives half as much on both occasions from the same aunt. How much does Jonathan receive altogether?

Add   £7.50 + £12.50 = £20.00

Divide   £20.00 ÷ 2 = £10.00

Jonathan receives **£10.00**

c. 'Mean' to Amount

If you are given the 'Mean', an Amount can be found.
Example:

> Gary's birthday is on Saturday. He receives birthday cards through the week (An Average of **6** a day over the week). How many did he receive on Thursday?

1. Find the Total - **Multiply** the 'Mean' by the number of days.
   $6 \times 5 = \mathbf{30}$
2. **Add** the given Amounts.
   $5 + 7 + 1 + 8 = \mathbf{21}$
3. **Subtract** the given Amounts from the Total.
   $30 - 21 = \mathbf{9}$

Day	Number of cards
Mon	5
Tue	7
Wed	1
Thurs	?
Fri	8

The 'Mean' is 6

He received 9 cards on Thursday.

Exercise 7: 2c   Score ☐

8) Year 6 conducted a survey on the flavour of milk shake they most liked.

   How many children liked vanilla? ....

Milk Shake	No. of pupils
Vanilla	?
Strawberry	23
Banana	14
Raspberry	6

The 'Mean' is 15

9) The Average spending of four girls was **£5.50**. Three of the girls spent **£3.20**, **£6.25** and **£5.10**. How much did the fourth girl spend? £ ....

10) The Average (Mean) age of seven children is **10 years**. The Average (Mean) age of six of the children is **9 years**. How old is the seventh child? .... years.

3. More Average Problems

Exercise 7: 3 Calculate the following: Score [ ]

These are the numbers of letters received by a small business each day for a week.

23   13   57   21   21

Find the following Average Values.   1) Mean ....

2) Mode .... 3) Median .... 4) Range ....

_ _

5) The 'Mean' Cost of five books is **£3.50**. What is the Total Cost?   £ ....

6) Another book is added which Costs **£6.50**. What is the new 'Mean' cost?   £ ....

_ _

Sanesh does a survey on how much tea his father drinks in one week. His father keeps a record, but forgets to write down how many cups he drank on Wednesday. He believes he drinks about **6 cups** a day (treat this as the 'Mean').

Day	Mon	Tues	Wed	Thurs	Fri	Sat	Sun
Cups of Tea	6	7	?	5	6	4	10

7) How many cups were drunk on Wednesday? .... cups.

8) What is the Median Value? .... cups.

9) What is the Range? ....

10) In the following week he restricts his tea drinking to a total of 21 cups. The new 'Mean' amount for that week is? .... cups.

Chapter Eight
BASES
1. What is a Base?

A Base is a pattern of counting. The name of the Base comes from the main counting unit.

The **Tens Number System** (Decimal System) or **Denary** is the basis for most counting. An **Abacus** can be used.

Example: $\boxed{\textbf{4,321} \text{ shown as } \textbf{Base 10}.}$

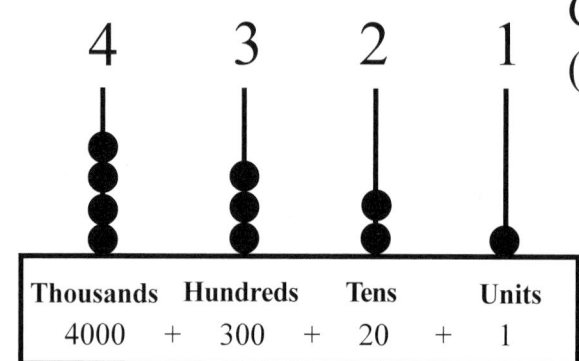

Counting in groups of ten (from 0 up to 9 in each column).

Four groups of **1000**
Three groups of **100**
Two groups of **10**
1 unit

The number as **Base 10** is $\boxed{4321_{10}}$

The Base is shown at the foot of the number.

2. Base 2 (Binary)

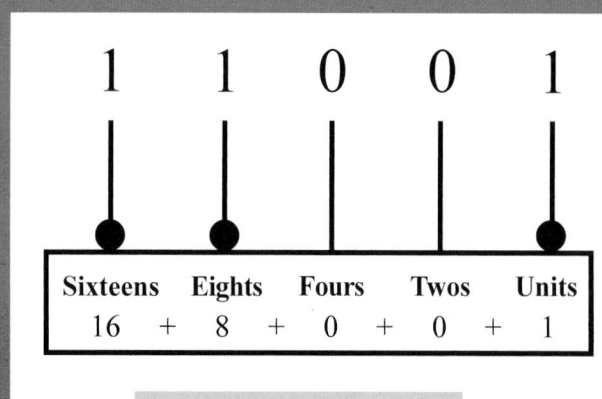

Base 2 is termed **Binary**. Counting in groups of two (Up to 1 in each column). Example:

$\boxed{\textbf{Convert } 25_{10} \text{ to Base 2.}}$

One group of **16**
One group of **8**
1 unit

$$25_{10} = 11001_2$$

Exercise 8: 1

Score

Convert from Base 10 to Base 2:

1) 10_{10} = ...$_2$

Eights	Fours	Twos	Units

2) 17_{10} = ...$_2$

Sixteens	Eights	Fours	Twos	Units

3) 7_{10} = ...$_2$

4) 12_{10} = ...$_2$

5) 31_{10} = ...$_2$

- -

Convert from Base 2 to Base 10:

6)

Eights	Fours	Twos	Units
1	1	1	1_2

= ....$_{10}$

7) 101_2 = ...$_{10}$

8) 110_2 = ...$_{10}$

9) 1011_2 = ...$_{10}$

10) 11101_2 = ...$_{10}$

Adding and Subtracting in Base 2.

It follows the normal pattern except each column can only show digits **0** or **1**. Examples:

Add 111_2 + 110_2

$$1\ 1\ 1_2$$
$$1\ 1\ 0_2 +$$
$$\overline{1\ 1\ 0\ 1_2}$$
$$\overline{1\ \ \ 1}$$

Base 10
7
6 +

13

$1 + 0 = 1$
Place 1 in column 1.
$1 + 1 = 2$
Place 0 in column 2, carry 1.
$1 + 1 + 1 = 3$
Place 1 in column 3, carry 1.
Place 1 in column 4.

Subtract 1001_2 - 110_2

$$^0\cancel{1}\overset{+2}{\cancel{0}}\ \overset{+2}{0}\ 1_2$$
$$^2\cancel{1}\ 1\ 0_2 -$$
$$\overline{0\ 0\ 1\ 1_2}$$

Base 10
9
6 -

3

$1 - 0 = 1$
Place 1 in column 1.
Borrow 2; $2 - 1 = 1$
Place 1 in column 2, pay back 1.
Borrow 2; $2 - 2 = 0$
Place 0 in column 3.
Place 0 in column 4.

CERTIFICATE
OF
ACHIEVEMENT
(Second)

This certifies.................................... has completed **Maths Book Two** successfully.

Overall Percentage Score Achieved.

%

Comment....................................

....

Signed ....
(teacher/parent/guardian)

Date ....